BARBER'S
GUIDE
TO
Life, Medicine, & Faith

Enjoy some lessons
from the barbers!

[signature]

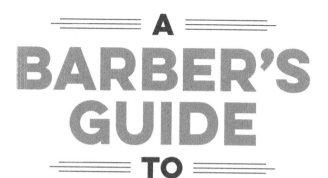

A
BARBER'S
GUIDE
TO
Life, Medicine, & Faith

MIKE NELSON, MD

INSPIRED BY MIKE READ
EDITED BY DR. H. DEAN THOMPSON

Printed in the United States of America.

All Biblical references are from the following book:
The New Oxford Annotated Bible, New Revised Standard Version, Fourth Edition, Oxford University Press

ISBN 978-0-9978189-0-1

First Edition

And Jesus answered them, "Those who are well have no need of a physician, but those who are sick. I have not come to call the righteous but sinners to repentance."

Luke 5: 31-32

CONTENTS

A
BARBER'S
GUIDE
TO
Life, Medicine, & Faith

FOREWORD

Mike Read was a generous, humble, kind barber. This book is as much a tribute to him as it is a guide to others. It is a tale of his legacy that neither he nor I may have ever dreamed of when our friendship began years ago.

Entering 'Mike's Barber Shop' on HWY 29 in Lilburn, Georgia, one might be taken back a bit by the rustic setting. Lawn chairs served as waiting seats, and blackboards donned the walls with Mike's shop rules and messages. I almost get teary eyed trying to describe a place and a time that are no longer present. Mike has since passed away, and the shop is now a Home Depot shopping center. Mike's Barber Shop was a throwback in time, as was the man who ran it.

It was in this shop, spending time with Mike, that I learned a lot of life lessons that I carry with me to this day. I grew up in a great family with wonderful parents, so I was not looking for a mentor. God is good and put a wonderful unexpected mentor in my life in the form of Mike, my barber, my friend.

In 7th grade I decided that to receive the flattop haircut that I desired, I would need to find a real barber, which led to my first interaction with Mike Read in the one chair barber shop named for him. My first time in his chair led to an exchange of possibly ten words between us. As Mike realized I was a fan of his talented haircuts and would be a regular customer, he began to ask about my interests. He quickly learned I was an athlete, which led to a quick friendship, as Mike loved sports. He was able to find a common interest, a skill key to his character as I observed his interactions with other customers/friends over the years.

An entrepreneur myself, I was a self-taught barber. I would cut the hair of my younger brother and many of my teammates. Rather than feeling threatened, Mike seized upon the common interest and made me his apprentice barber. I became a licensed apprentice barber, which allowed me to cut hair legally in any barber shop in the state of Georgia. This occurred in 1992, when I was eighteen years old. During my apprenticeship I was able to fill in for Mike while he travelled. While attending Presbyterian College I served as the unofficial dorm barber, which helped me pay for my books, earn spending money, and develop numerous friendships. Who would have known that barbering was the perfect training for my future occupation as a physician? When I graduated from the Medical College of Georgia in 2000, I'm not sure who was more proud in the crowd: my wife, my parents, or Mike.

After graduating from medical school, I entered an Internal Medicine and Pediatrics combined residency at the University of Cincinnati. I was trained well with the aid of great attendings, grueling hours, and challenging patients. This paradigm is common to many residencies. Although medical school and residency trained me well for the medical aspect of my future job, it did not prepare me for some of the practical aspects of practice management while maintaining balance at home.

Upon graduation from residency in 2004, I was given the opportunity to open a new hospital-owned Internal Medicine and Pediatrics practice with my friend from medical school, Matt Baker, MD. He and I were able to carefully organize our practice and workday. After ten years in this practice, I realized that a lot of the practice patterns and principles were derived from my time in the barber shop years earlier.

The first version of this book included the lessons from the barber shop and the medical correlates, but it didn't seem complete. As I was writing this book, I envisioned my three sons as part of the audience, which makes this endeavor of writing very personal to me. As a Christian man I have enjoyed sharing biblical study with my boys at home and with my church primarily as an adult Sunday School teacher. Adding the biblical correlate to the barber's lessons made this book then seem complete.

By no means am I a practice management expert, nor am I a renowned theologian. I have found a way to be a part of a successful medical practice, while balancing my commitments at home and church. I write this book to share with you the lessons learned in an American institution, the barber shop.

CHAPTER ONE

Shop Hours

Time management is an elusive and difficult task for many professionals. Taped to 'Mike's Barber Shop' door was a simple sign:

SHOP HOURS
Shades open: Open
Shades closed: Closed

It was a humorous sight to me at the time, but I often think back to the lesson in that simple sign.

Mike's shop hours were practical to his customers. As the customers drove by the shop they would know if Mike was available or not. Towards the end of the day, he would draw the shades and finish the haircuts for those in the shop at the time. In fairness Mike was a hard worker, and he worked predictable hours for his customers, but he also knew he needed to get home each night for his family and his own sake.

In a barber shop as with many businesses, ten people could walk in during the last ten minutes and keep Mike there an extra two hours. Rather than debate whose haircut was more urgent, he knew his loyal customers would return another day if the shades were drawn. For those not loyal to his services, Mike did not seem to worry.

Although I knew Mike's shop hours, I did not learn the lesson in that simple sign until years later. During my medical school and residency days, I was not in a position to set my own hours. Residency would lead to one-hundred hour work weeks at times, which made anything less seem like light work. It was't until I grew my own practice that I realized the need and importance of Mike's shop hours.

I'm not sure my patients would find much humor in me posting office hours the same way

Mike did. I have standard office hours, and my partner in practice and I try to cover each other's time off to ensure access for our patients. With that said, I have some standards that help me maintain balance between time at work and home.

First, appointments are an expectation I have for my patients. Do I turn away a walk-in patient with chest pain or wheezing? No, but I do turn patients away with a cold to come back later in the day with an appointment. It is hard enough to stay on schedule with appointments made, but it is nearly impossible if a lot of walk-in patients arrive. Appointments keep me productive all day, rather than being busy at the end of the day into the evening.

Second, I understand that ill patients will need to be seen each day. I try to anticipate this by maintaining many urgent visit appointment slots that cannot be filled until the day of service. Mondays and Fridays are huge days for urgent visits; therefore, these days get many more time slots for urgent visits and less time slots for routine visits and annual physicals. Are there days when people aren't sick and don't need those open visits? Sure, some days end up light due to this strategy, but it is the price I pay to fulfill my obligation to my patients to be available.

Third, my home obligations change day to day, which requires planning. I have truly enjoyed being a husband and father of three boys. If I didn't embrace Mike's shop hours lesson, I could have easily missed out on one of my biggest pleasures, my family. It has been a blast coaching my boys in sports and attending their different activities. On a day with an event, I simply cut off my schedule an hour early. I still see those that need me that day, but I also see my kids grow up, and I remain in a healthy marriage.

In all honesty there are days when my patients get their call backs later at night or the non-urgent questions get answered the next morning, but my patients seem to understand that I too have a family life.

Fourth, I leave town for vacations. I truly love my town and community, but to get away with my family, I do need to literally get away. As a family we take a number of long weekend excursions, but we also routinely go to Hilton Head for a week each summer. The time away allows me to reconnect with my wife and sons, but it also allows me to recharge my battery for my patients. I am much more productive and helpful when I take periodic breaks.

It is very easy in any workplace to bury one's head in the sand and work nonstop. I got a chance to work this way in residency for four years. Although I wouldn't trade the training I received in Cincinnati, I did learn that working one-hundred hour weeks were neither healthy nor enjoyable. When it was my turn to plan my day, it was an opportunity to employ the barber's first lesson, posted on the door. Thank you, Mike, for this lesson.

Thus the heavens and the earth were finished, and all their multitude. And on the seventh day God finished the work that he had done, and he rested . . . So God blessed the seventh day and hallowed it, because on it God rested from all the work that he had done in creation.

Genesis 2:1-3

....

Remember the sabbath day, and keep it holy. Six days you shall labor and do all your work. But the seventh day is a sabbath to the Lord your God; you shall not do any work . . .

Exodus 20: 8-10

....

Just as the barber's first lesson highlights the need for rest, God too saw this need for himself as noted in Genesis. If God saw the need for rest, then we too should see the importance of this simple act. Too often I take this basic need for granted, yet in times when I was expected to work thirty-six hour stretches, sleep was a luxury. Our cognition is clearly affected by sleep or lack thereof. At the end of a long day, one routine task can seemingly take twice as long. Children actually can have a paradoxical reaction to lack of sleep as they often become hyperactive when bedtime is long past gone. I see this with my own children, and I hear this complaint often from the parents of my patients. Rest clearly is important from our earliest days.

The fourth commandment of God's Ten Commandments again states God's desire for us to take a day of rest as noted in Exodus. To view the Ten Commandments as constraining rules is a shortsighted view. God gave man the Ten Commandments as a field guide of sorts for a happy and fulfilling life.

Too often our culture is encouraging constant activity whether that be work or play. God saw the need to set aside one day out of seven to rest, reflect, and worship God.

I have often taken pause to reflect upon my occupational need to work on some Sundays. Should I not work on Sundays without regard to emergent patient needs or on-call coverage duties? Jesus gives us good answers to this question in the second chapter of Mark and thirteenth chapter of Luke.

One Sabbath he (Jesus) was going through the grainfields; and as they made their way his disciples began to pluck heads of grain. The Pharisees said to him, "Look, why are they doing what is not lawful on the sabbath?"

. . . Then he said to them, "The sabbath was made for humankind, and not humankind for the sabbath; so the Son of Man is lord even of the sabbath."

Mark 2: 23-24, 27-28

....

Now he (Jesus) was teaching in one of the synagogues on the sabbath. And just then there appeared a women with a spirit that had crippled her for eighteen years. She was bent over and was quite unable to stand up straight. When Jesus saw her, he called her over and said, "Woman, you are set free from your ailment." When he laid his hands on her, immediately she stood up straight and began praising God. But the leader of the synagogue, indignant because Jesus had cured on the sabbath, kept saying to the crowd, "There are six days on which work ought to be done; on the Sabbath day." But the Lord answered him and said, "You hypocrites!

Does not each of you on the Sabbath untie his ox or his donkey from the manger, and lead it away to give it water? And ought not this women, a daughter of Abraham whom Satan bound for eighteen long years, be set free from this bondage on the Sabbath day?" When he said this, all his opponents were put to shame . . .

Luke 13: 10-17

It seems that if work is in an effort to fulfill the needs of others, then it is justified and not contrary to the fourth commandment. Scripture doesn't always conveniently give specific answers to our questions, but for my medical work dilemma, it appears Luke, the physician, gave a clear example of Jesus' appropriate healing on a sabbath.

When I work on a Sunday, it is in a call situation where urgent needs of the patients are being met, but non-urgent medical needs are attended to on other days of the week. I have often been asked why we don't have office hours on the weekend. The answer is that I need time to rest, time with my family, and time with God in worship. I hope that my staff has those same needs met each weekend as well. My patients seem to understand these needs. Mike the barber understood these needs. Clearly the Lord our Father foresaw this need for us and expected that it be recognized.

Thank you, Lord, for providing for us rest.

CHAPTER TWO

I'll Rush,
When It's Your Turn

I have never encountered an occupation that doesn't occasionally get off schedule and fall behind, causing people the need to wait. My occupation, unfortunately, is notorious for this, and each of my patients likely would concur with that statement. There are many reasons that this falling behind occurs, which is not the point of this lesson.

For multiple summers I also had the pleasure of working with Joe Beatty at 'Joe's Barber Shop.' Joe was a retired police officer and jail warden who opened his lifelong dream, a barber shop. His shop was full of sports and fishing memorabilia, with either Celtic or 1950's music playing in the background. To this day I still am amazed that I can recite 1950's song lyrics when I hear those songs on the radio.

Barber shop customer flows were very erratic. Joe and I could sit for hours waiting for customers, and then we could cut hair for hours without any break in sight. It was always great if one customer was finishing when the next arrived, but usually customers would come in clusters and someone would need to wait. Invariably someone would tell Joe to hurry up to try to shorten their wait time. Whenever I heard this comment, I knew the next line from Joe, who without hesitation would say, "I am going to take my time with my current customer, but when it is your turn, I will go really fast." Joe would then chuckle to take away the sting of his pointed quip. His message was usually heard loud and clear.

To succumb to the time pressures at the expense of quality was not acceptable to Joe unless the customer wanted quick, poor-quality service. When given that option I never saw a customer choose to have a quick, poor-quality haircut. Joe was comfortable seeing customers leave that didn't have time to wait. Most returned on another day when they had more time or when the shop was quiet.

As a physician, I too have to deal with the understandable frustrations of waiting patients. I have three children, and I have waited with them at a doctor's office. It is hard to keep them occupied without their tearing down the office. After waiting with my children, I expected a good, quality medical visit. Poor quality in medicine is unacceptable to me not only as a patient, but also as a medical provider.

When my schedule gets backed up, I frequently hear Joe in my head saying that no one wants to wait a long time only to receive quick, poor-quality service. There are no clocks in my exam rooms, and I no longer wear a watch. I do not want patients to ever perceive me rushing through the visit. It is important for me to remain patient with the patients, which allows me to give good care and show care for my patients.

How do I maintain any semblance of a schedule

with this mantra? I do have a clock in my work area viewed frequently between patients, so I do know if I am falling behind schedule. There is also a bit of an internal clock in me that helps me know how I am doing on time. In reality some visits are predictably quick and others are predictably long, and I have staff that know well how to weave these visits together each day. I also have a forty-five minute lunch break that usually helps me take a breather, get a quick bite to eat, and feel caught up again.

With all that said, there are times when patients need an extraordinary amount of time from me at the expense of the rest of that half-day schedule. A grieving spouse, a very ill child, complicated family dynamics, and cancer patients are a few examples of long visits sometimes unanticipated. As I face the waiting patients to follow, I enter with an apology, but I try not to linger on the obvious fact that I am late. When questioned concerning my delay, I am unable to give specific details due to patient confidentiality, but I do try to assure them that on a day they need extra time, I will give them that time too. As the barbers showed me, if the frustrated individuals are unable to deal with my style, they are free to find another physician, and if pressed too hard, sometimes I have to tactfully remind them of that freedom.

Luckily I have many very loyal patients who understand that occasional wait times are part of the package they receive in me. They often acknowledge that I listen well to them and do not rush, and they appreciate that approach. I certainly have lost some patients over a long wait time, but thanks to Joe, I learned many more patients appreciate quality over speed. In 'Joe's Barber Shop' I never gave a quick, poor-quality haircut, and hopefully in my medical practice I have been boldly patient.

....

Now as they went on their way, he (Jesus) entered a certain village, where a women named Martha welcomed him into her home. She had a sister named Mary, who sat at the Lord's feet and listened to what he was saying. But Martha was distracted by her many tasks; so she came to him and asked, "Lord, do you not care that my sister has left me to do all the work by myself? Tell her then to help me." But the Lord answered her, "Martha, Martha, you are worried and distracted by many things; there is need of only one thing. Mary has chosen the better part, which will not be taken away from her."

Luke 10: 38-42

Jesus was not about to rush through his ministry just as Joe would not compromise a haircut for the sake of speed. Too often in life I am tempted to rush through activities and events, and it takes hearing Joe in my head or remembering the story of Mary and Martha for me to remember to slow down and enjoy each moment. Certainly Martha's work was needed as well, but obviously not at the expense of spending time with her Lord.

The last chapter focused on taking time for rest and also taking time for worship. It dovetails nicely with the need to slow down our moments in life for greater meaning and enjoyment. These verses make clear the importance for patience during our time with the Lord in prayer, Bible study, worship, and so on. It was easy for Martha to be distracted, and she was in the presence of the Lord. Think how much easier it is for us to be distracted from our time with the Lord in the age of smart phones, constant TV programming, twenty-four-hour news cycles, and mass marketing. It is easy to become distracted from our daily lives and, more worrisome, our time for God; therefore, our moments with God must be very intentional and consistent. A routine relationship with our Lord helps to tamp down the distractions.

To all of our distracting activities, I'm sure the Lord would be happy for us to use Joe's line, "I rush when it is your turn." I strive each day to not rush through my interactions with patients, friends, and family. More importantly I see the need to also patiently seek out my relationship with the Lord. To Joe, Mary, and Martha, I appreciate the lesson of patience.

CHAPTER THREE

When You First Start, Don't Take Off Too Much

I was in my senior year in high school when Mike floated the idea of my becoming his apprentice. Mike had known for years that I barbered in my basement. I would cut my brothers' hair, as well as my friends' and teammates' hair. I was no where near what I would call a professional, yet since I was of course young and invincible, when he asked to be his apprentice barber, I jumped at the idea.

Mike hailed from a small town in Oakland, Illinois, although you would not be able to tell that from Mike's deep southern accent. A high-school reunion was approaching that summer, and Mike was trying to problem-solve as he had no coverage for his one-chair barber shop. Enter Mike Nelson as an apprentice barber, and he didn't even have to change the sign 'Mike's Barber Shop.'

Now when Mike went back home, he really went home for a while. A friend or family member would let Mike stay in what sounded like a small trailer or RV. Mike's plan was to go to this high-school reunion and visit family for one month in the summer between my senior year of high school and freshman year of college. It was my first big job, not to mention my first profession. Mike used to always say, "It is good to have a trade in your back pocket." No matter where life took me, Mike felt confident that he had given me the assurance that I could always barber if needed.

After agreeing to become Mike's apprentice barber, I assumed some training sessions would ensue to prepare me for this adventure. I don't recall that any sessions ever happened; in fact, I recall becoming a bit unnerved that training hadn't occurred as Mike was soon to depart. I must have asked Mike about this matter just prior to his turning the shop keys over to me, and I vividly remember his only pointer: "When you first start, don't take off too much."

I wonder if that first customer on my first day running the shop knew my initial angst. My first few haircuts must have taken an hour apiece. Mike had a loyal clientele, many of whom were retired, so they did not point out my lack of speed. I did luckily have a gift for talking to strangers even at a young age, so hopefully I shared some entertaining conversation with them as they received the longest haircut of their life.

As time went on I became more and more comfortable with my new profession. It was probably a blessing that Mike did not encumber me with a lot of do's and don'ts for the technique of barbering. Over time I certainly developed good technique mostly by trial and error. At some point I must have violated the only rule Mike gave me of not taking off too much hair. My custom had been to turn the customer around at the end of the haircut and ask if that is the haircut he wanted. Most would nod, and some would ask for a little more hair off here or there, but one answered my end of haircut review with a riddle: "Do you know the difference between a good haircut and a bad haircut?" Puzzled, I answered, "No." He responded, "Two weeks." I must have taken off too much hair; Mike later laughed as I retold this story to him.

One might wonder how this bit of advice to not take off too much hair could relate to an Internist and Pediatrician. It is clear how it might relate to a surgeon, right? Often patients present too many complaints to realistically address in one visit. I have found myself saying, "I can do six complaints quickly and likely poorly, or you can choose the three most pressing concerns, and I will do a good and thorough job." I have yet to have someone pick the former option, nor have I found someone who got upset with the reality of the need to hone down the objective of the visit.

Part of the beauty of Pediatrics is that the visits are routinely very focused. That the child is ill, has an earache, or has behavioral issues are common complaints for a visit. Usually the pressing time constraint is not mine, but rather that the child and parent don't want to remain confined in the exam room for too long.

It is the Internal Medicine patient who can present multiple complaints in a single visit. Coming out of residency, I was in the habit of admitting very complex patients with multiple medical problems. During an admission I would need to make sure I was attending to all the underlying problems, while also trying to treat the acute problem leading to the need for admission to the hospital. I still had that mentality early in my outpatient practice, and like my first day in the barber shop, those visits were likely the longest of that patient's life.

I learned how to go into an Internal Medicine follow-up visit with a game plan. Chart organization of current medications, chronic medical

problems and prior surgeries, self-injurious be-
haviors (such as smoking and drinking), and pertinent family history can save a lot of time and
need only updating. My usual visit includes
briefly catching up socially (quite enjoyable),
quickly reviewing chronic active problems and
adjusting treatment as needed, insuring updated
cancer screening/vaccinations/health maintenance
issues, and allowing time for new interval complaints. As it is, this is quite a complex visit at
times, but if organized, it can actually fit into a fif-
teen to twenty-five minute timeframe. Lucky for
me, my staff knows who routinely takes on the
twenty-five minute side of this range and sched-
ules appropriately.

Although some adult visits are quite long, these
same patients also come in for acute problem visits.
The challenge is to allow the shorter focused visits
be just that. On those visits they neither desire nor
need all the chronic active issues addressed, and it
is my job to attend to the problem at hand. These
visits help to balance the day.

With all this said, it is still important to take care of the patient regardless of my organization tips above. One of the difficulties of my job is that the patients are not all skilled in prioritizing or maybe don't know how to effectively communicate concerns in an efficient manner. It is not uncommon to complete a long extensive Internal Medicine follow-up visit and, while literally while going out of the door, be asked by the patient about recent chest pain. I take a deep breath, reenter the room, and restart a very important problem-based visit. The patients with all the co-morbid issues such as hypertension, diabetes, and high cholesterol are the very ones at the highest risk for underlying cardiac disease in this example. One of my former Internal Medicine attendings, Dr. Philip Schmitt, used to say, "Rule out that which could kill the patient first." I always hear him in my head when confronted with that situation of a potentially serious complaint presented to me at what would seem like the end of the visit.

Dr. Schmitt's reminder is the fine print disclaimer statement for the general advice of this chapter.

....

No testing has overtaken you that is not common to everyone. God is faithful, and he will not let you be tested beyond your strength, but with the testing he will also provide the way out so that you may be able to endure it.

1 Corinthians 10: 13

....

A chapter title such as "When You First Start, Don't Take Off Too Much" might make you think the Biblical correlate was to be related to circumcision, but that would be too predictable. The barber and doctor lessons are those of trying to resist the temptation of taking on more than that day's visit would allow. Paul in his letter to the Corinthians reassures me that God too understands the human feeling of being overwhelmed.

Paul gives me confidence that God will not give me more than I can handle. In the verses leading up to the often quoted 1 Corinthians 10: 13, Paul compares the failures of the Jewish generation left in the wilderness noted in Exodus to the distractions encountered by the Corinthians of that time. Paul gave examples of idolatry, sexual immorality, and complaining as evil temptations, which still seem very relevant today as well.

As often as I have thought of this verse in times of struggle, I have yet to reflect on the first line, "No testing has overtaken you that is not common to everyone." It strikes me how we are all in the same boat of living in a land that is wrought with temptations that can separate us from our relationship with God, just as the Jews were separated from the promised land due to their struggles with temptations. As we are all in the same predicament, it is paramount that we assist each other to live lives pleasing to God. There is comfort that even though my current struggles seem unique to me, Paul instructs that our challenges are common to others as well.

There are certainly days that seem overwhelming, even while trying to be mindful of not taking on too much for one day or one visit. When those days or moments occur that seem beyond my capacity, I am reminded that God is aware of these burdensome times, and He faithfully will not give me more to deal with than I can handle. Thank you, Paul, for giving me confidence in times of struggle.

CHAPTER FOUR

No Fad Haircuts

Upon walking into 'Mike's Barber Shop,' one would see the walls decorated with chalkboards which Mike Read used to communicate with and unintentionally entertain his customers. Honestly, I can't remember all that was written on the chalkboards, but I do remember one constant message: "No Fad Haircuts." Professionally Mike wasn't about to let someone walk out of his shop with a haircut he wasn't proud to say he performed.

To this day my family members still remember Mike's simple rule written in very clear terms. It certainly brings forth a chuckle when mentioned, although we also never saw someone with a fad haircut walking out of Mike's shop. It must have put Mike in an uncomfortable position enough times to cause that rule to grace the all-powerful chalkboards. That clear communication must have served Mike well, as that rule never left the chalkboard as other writings would come and go.

If people know where you stand on an issue, then there is no debate. If it is clear which services are not available in businesses that serve others, people will know to go somewhere else for that service. Mike did not stop people from getting fad haircuts; he just stopped having to consider giving them.

I had a friend who used Mike Read as his barber as well. He once asked for a Mohawk haircut after seeing on the chalkboard "no fad haircuts" for years. Mike proceeded to cut his hair, but my friend was disappointed to see he received a skinny flattop haircut. To this day I can still see my friend's reaction later that day to his Mohawk, Mike Read style. He was a little shocked and embarrassed that he got a skinny flattop. I was not at all surprised, as I knew the rule.

It is okay to draw a line in the sand professionally. Be clear and intentional about this. Matt Baker, MD, my friend and partner in practice, and I decided we would not agree to a practice of avoiding vaccinations or delaying vaccinations for children. Our practice of combined Internal Medicine and Pediatrics is definitely weighted more in Pediatrics, with 60-70% of our patients being children. With that said, we could not imagine trying to practice in an environment where our patients are unvaccinated for illnesses that can be very debilitating and severe. We decided early in our practice that as advocates of our pediatric patients, we needed to be firm with the need to vaccinate. We would feel awful if one of our patients contracted a serious illness that could have been avoided with appropriate vaccination. Also out of respect for those parents who vaccinate their children, we wanted them to feel comfortable that all the children in the waiting room were also following the same CDC recommended shot schedule.

One might ask how we are able to enforce such a

policy. It is actually quite simple. Expectant parents come to interview us prior to having their first child, which is a required free consultation prior to accepting their future children as patients. During that visit we clearly ask if they plan to vaccinate their children per the CDC recommendations. If they answer yes, then I explain that we are on the same page and reassure them that I choose the same treatment for my own children and require it of my other patients. If they have reservations about vaccinations, then I try to give them the information that I know on the subject and lead them to investigate that decision using information from sources such as the CDC website and Children's Hospital of Philadelphia website (Q&A format). I am clear with wavering new parents that if they choose not to vaccinate their children, then they need to find another Pediatrician who accepts that choice. At the end of the day, the parents have every right to choose as they prefer, but I don't have to agree to practice in a way that I find unacceptable.

Vaccines are just one example for the need to be intentional about professional lines that are drawn.

When feeling conflicted about something within one's profession, it is important to take thoughtful consideration and choose a plan of action that is fair, clear, and consistent. If that plan of action is not what patients or customers desire, then they can go elsewhere for their desired service. Whether it is fad haircuts or unvaccinated children, these situations still occur, just not with the blessings of the Mikes.

....

Then Jesus was led up by the Spirit into the wilderness to be tempted by the devil. He fasted forty days and forty nights, and afterwards he was famished. The tempter (Satan) came and said to him, "If you are the Son of God, command these stones to become loaves of bread." But he answered, "It is written, 'One does not live by bread alone, but by every word that comes from the mouth of God.'"

Then the devil took him to the holy city and placed him on the pinnacle of the temple, saying to him, "If you are the Son of God, throw yourself down; for it is written, 'He will command his angels concerning you,' and 'On their hands they will bear you up, so that you will not dash your foot against a stone.'" Jesus said to him, "Again it is written, 'Do not put the Lord your God to the test.'"

Again, the devil took him to a very high mountain and showed him all the kingdoms of the world and their splendor; and he said to him, "All these I will give you, if you will fall down and worship me." Jesus said to him, "Away with you, Satan! For it is written, 'Worship the Lord your God, and serve only him.'" Then the devil left him, and suddenly angels came and waited on him.

Matthew 4: 1-11

The book of Matthew reminds us that, yes, even Jesus was tempted to sin by none other than Satan. It is quite remarkable that our Lord and God was encouraged by the Holy Spirit to experience the temptation of sin. Our God incarnate showed exactly how to deal with sin. Jesus was one with God's word in the form of the Old Testament, exemplifying what is meant by the living word.

Now did Satan try to tempt Jesus on his best day when he was well rested and well fed? Of course not: Satan waited for Jesus to be famished and likely exhausted after forty days and nights of fasting in the wilderness. Satan started with the obvious desire for food and tempted Jesus to use his power to turn stones to bread, but Satan increases the pressure when coercing Jesus to have God save him from danger.

Finally Satan goes for the greatest temptation of power and riches and offers Jesus all the kingdoms of the world. Each time Jesus without hesitation gives Satan scripture to rebuke Satan's temptations. On likely Jesus' most physically demanding days on earth to date, he responded perfectly to this world's greatest temptation.

It is important to note where these verses fall in the book of Matthew. Prior to being tempted, Jesus was baptized by John in the wilderness. Just after Jesus' temptation in the wilderness, he begins his ministry. It is comforting to know that the wonderful ministry of Jesus is free of Satan's influence, as he shed temptation to sin before embarking on ministry. Many times today the model of extreme testing prior to acceptance into that group remain; examples of significant challenge prior to acceptance include Navy Seal and Army Ranger training, medical school and residency training, football summer two-a-day practices, the police academy, presidential campaigns, seminary, and student teaching, just to name a few. God had Jesus well prepared for his ministry, cloaked with God's word, baptism, and the Holy Spirit. Jesus' temptation in the wilderness gives evidence of such readiness prior to embarking on his great ministry.

As I am tested professionally and personally, it is comforting to know that even Jesus experienced this common human situation. I often tell my teenage patients as they head into high school to be prepared for the temptations of drugs or alcohol, and I recommend they have a game plan for how to deal with that situation, such as telling the tempter, "My doctor recommends that I not do that." God obviously knows that temptation to sin is part of this world, as He encouraged His only Son to experience this human condition in extreme. Jesus was prepared to respond to Satan armored with God's word. I know I fall short of God's will in times of testing, but I do feel prepared with God's word and guided by the Holy Spirit.

CHAPTER FIVE

Blending is the Key to a Good Haircut

In addition to being such a good person, Mike Read was a great barber. If it weren't for his crisp haircuts, many wouldn't have ever gotten to know Mike personally.

Barbering was the vehicle God gave Mike to make a large impact in this world. As I would watch Mike cut hair, he would occasionally say that blending was the key to a good haircut, and boy, was he good at it. His haircuts always seemed perfectly done.

Blending a haircut is harder than it sounds. Most trims require one length to be blended to the next length, and here in lies the skill of barbering. I was always amazed how well Mike could taper hair in the back and seamlessly blend the sides to the top hair.

After breakfast on Eli's thirteenth birthday, my son requested a fresh haircut. I took him downstairs to my basement barber shop and gladly fulfilled his request. During the finishing touches of the haircut, he reminded me that a good haircut requires the customer to remain still during some of the more delicate portions of the trim. His quick movement during the edging of his neck hairline reminded me of this partnership between customer and barber. Of course some blending ensued.

Not only can mistakes be made in barbering, but I would argue that mistakes will occur in all professions. I sometimes explain to interviewing expecting parents that when humans are involved, there is going to be human error. Obviously in medicine the goal is minimize error to the lowest rate possible.

Part of the solution to minimizing human error lies in a partnership with the patient to help keep me accountable. Whenever a patient has a lab drawn, I ask the patient to call me after one week from the time of the lab draw, if they haven't heard from me first. Most lab results should return within a week, and I try to call the patient with an explanation of the labs and any medical changes based on the the lab results, if needed. Occasionally the results aren't faxed to me, or I am slow to review, or I have the wrong patient phone number(s) in the chart; all can be remedied by the patient's calling for results. For more urgent results I give a different notification expectation; for example, with jaundice-level results in a five day old, I will call with results and treatment plan, if necessary, by the end of the afternoon.

Blending also included overcoming mistakes within the haircut. Of the minimal skill training Mike gave me, blending in mistakes within the haircut was an invaluable barbering skill that I unfortunately needed all to often when I first started barbering. If I followed one of the skill tips of not cutting off too much hair, then I still had some hair to work with when blending over a mistake. With the advancement of barbering skill, the barber's "Whoops!" moments are easily corrected without the customer ever noticing. I suppose with time my moments of inadvertent blending were not accompanied with my quick-to-redden Swedish cheeks.

One might ask how blending a haircut might relate to medicine? Problem based visits require obtaining as much information possible through history and physical exam to formulate a working diagnosis and treatment plan. Histories and physicals are especially challenging in Pediatrics, when many of my patients can't speak for themselves nor fully comply with the physical exam. We are often at the mercy of the accompanying adult's (i.e. Mom, Dad, Grandparent) ability to convey the details of the illness or problem, and then sometimes act as a holder/wrestler for our squirmy patients during the exam. Due to the variability of the information available via history and physical, the resultant working diagnosis is very fluid. The diagnosis may change based on patient response or lack thereof to treatment, new information from labs or imaging, consultants opinion, or my own review while charting or driving down the road (I carry my patients with me in my thoughts sometimes). Blending in medicine translates to being flexible to change the working diagnosis and treatment plan as dictated by the fore mentioned additional insight.

When a haircut wasn't going as expected Mike Read was comfortable changing to a slightly different cut, so too in medicine a working diagnosis is not a final diagnosis. The good doctors know this well and are open to change direction in an effort to help their patient.

It is also important to set expectations for myself and the patient to adhere. This means if I expect fevers to resolve after forty-eight hours on treatment, then when the fevers persist greater than forty-eight hours, 1. the patient or caregiver must notify me of persistent fever, and 2. I must respond with a different treatment plan. I routinely tell patients that I only get to see a snapshot in time, so it is important for them to notify me if they are getting worse or not responding as expected. With that said, if the expectation is set that it may take up to forty-eight hours for a treatment to be effective, then the patient, the caregivers, and I need to allow the treatment proper time to work, supporting the patient as necessary while waiting.

During my barbering career I did run into one hairstyle that I could never seem to blend well, the dreaded comb-over. As some men age and bald, they don't embrace the thinning hairline and choose to grow out and comb over hair from one side over to the other side to cover-up the deficiency. It was difficult to trim the side hair without disturbing the hair destined for the flop to the other side; I could never get it quite right to my satisfaction. One day I had a relatively young man, which at this point in my life means mid-forties, enter the barber shop with a come-over. I'll never forget his haircut request, "My wife says for me to have you fix my hairstyle." Finally, I was given cart-blanche to fix my least favorite hairstyle. I cut off the comb-over! It felt so liberating, and in my opinion he looked so much better. He initially didn't seem to agree with my sentiment, but returned days later with his wife's thanks for my handiwork. One comb-over successfully blended, thousands more to go.

It seems in medicine there are disease states or medical conditions that seem to have no hope. Unfortunately I have seen patients endure strokes, cancers, and other terminal conditions that did not improve. On the other hand, I have seen patients that I thought there was no hope for improvement, and they seemed to make a full recovery. The only way for me to reconcile this clinical dilemma of anticipated outcomes in apparent poor medical circumstances is to surrender the outcome responsibility to God. In the meantime, my job is to support the patient and family of the patient to the best of my ability. To blend the unblendable situation may occasionally lead to a heroic recovery, but often it leads to a comfortable death or embracing a new normal medical status, accepting the setback.

Thank you Mike for teaching me how be fluid in a situation that is ever changing.

Then Pharisees and scribes came to Jesus from Jerusalem and said, "Why do your disciples break the tradition of the elders? For they do not wash their hands before they eat."

Then he (Jesus) called the crowd to him and said to them, "Listen and understand: it is not what goes into the mouth that defiles a person, but it is what comes out of the mouth that defiles."

But Peter said to him, "Explain this parable to us." Then he (Jesus) said, "Are you also still without understanding? Do you not see that whatever goes into the mouth enters the stomach, and goes out into the sewer? But what comes out of the mouth proceeds from the heart, and this is what defiles. For out of the heart come evil intentions, murder, adultery, fornication, theft, false witness, slander. These are what defile a person, but to eat with unwashed hands does not defile."

Matthew 15: 1-2, 10-11, 15-20

The barber and doctor examples deal with how to avoid, minimize, and manage professional error.

God had a powerful new approach to deal with the chronic problem of religious error; his name was Jesus. It is hard to understand how following God's word can lead to any form of error, but when the law becomes greater than the intention of the law, error follows. Part of Jesus' mission was to redirect the guidance of God's law to get back to it's original intention.

Matthew's reference to Jesus redefining God's law is one of many biblical examples of Jesus trying to put God's meaning and intention back into the guide of the law. I personally love these verses, as it reminds me of my Grandma Nelson. She used to always say, "If you can't say something nice about someone, then don't say anything at all." As words come out that go against my Grandma's and Jesus' guidance, I feel these verses on my heart, and it helps to redirect my words and thoughts.

Jesus helped to redirect the worship of law, rather than the worship of God with the guidance of the law. The Pharisees were a sect of Judaism encumbered most heavily with the law, so it was common for the Pharisees to press Jesus on the law. After

Jesus' crucifixion, He transformed a very prominent Pharisee, Saul, who was actively persecuting the new Christians, into the apostle Paul, who championed Jesus' ministry message. Paul went on to continue to redefine God's word, which he knew very well, using Jesus and the Holy Spirit to guide him.

Again, when humans are involved there will be human error. It is important to anticipate that error will occur in an effort to help minimize and eliminate error as much as possible. God knew there was error in religion, and He sent his only Son to redirect the message. The Holy Spirit now is available to all to guide one's thoughts, words, worship, and deeds; and for that I am thankful, because I sure need it.

CHAPTER SIX

Mamas Are Always Right

As Mike Read would cut the hair of children, it was always via direct order of their mothers. If a child self ordered a particular haircut, Mike would always look to the mom for their approval. Mike usually knew his regular adult customers' haircut, and he would not routinely spin them around at the end of the haircut for their approval. Children were never done until Mike received the okay from their mothers.

Looking back on Mike's interactions with children brings back memories of his unique approach with kids. He certainly did not use any different voice, faces, or gimmicks.

He treated these young customers like young men, no matter their age. This may have been exactly as the children would have it, as this was their time to get a "big boy haircut." Most children sat still and seemed mesmerized likely due to the resemblance of Mike's deep Southern voice to Eeyore, Winnie the Pooh's friend. For the young customers who couldn't behave, I imagine Mike would simply ask their mom to bring them back when they were able to stay still for a haircut. Mike had a gentle way of serving those who wanted to be there, and allowing those who didn't want to be there to go somewhere else, no matter their age.

This chapter title is a line from the great Ray Baker, MD, who trained me while on the Pediatric Wards at Cincinnati Children's Hospital. Dr. Baker had a wonderful warm approach to Pediatrics and to training those who would soon be delivering similar care. He is a practical Pediatrician who impressed upon me to listen to mamas, because as he would say, "Mamas are always right." In my daily work with Pediatric patients, I routinely hear Dr. Ray Baker in my head as Mothers provide me with their children's medical history.

Now it may seem like an easy premise to listen to the mothers for a medical history, but it is not always as easy as it sounds. Some of the histories are very long and convoluted, and it is my job to try to sort out the pertinent points and make some medical pattern from the information provided. Out of their love and concern, many times maternal history is laced with a lot of emotion that can sometimes be tempting to dismiss.

An appointment with the doctor for an illness or problem usually comes with an anticipated diagnosis by the mothers. Sometimes the mamas are spot on, and I am happy for them to be right. It is my job to go beyond the anticipated diagnosis and ask the mamas what makes them think their child has a particular illness, collect the pertinent history, and perform an appropriate exam. An example of this would be the all-too-often-suspected ear infection. Pulling on the ear is the usual history that leads moms to conclude their children have an ear infection, but many illnesses include the symptom of earache. Earaches occur with middle ear infections as expected, but teething, external otitis, TMJ, mastoiditis, posterior and pre-auricular lymphadenitis, and even tonsillitis occasionally are accompanied with earache. Now the mamas are right that their child has an earache, but it is my job to decide from which etiology the pain hails, as each diagnosis comes with a different treatment. Of course in Pediatrics there have been some interesting initial complaints and subsequent findings. I have fielded complaints of finger nail in eye, lots of swallowed coins, lots of objects in ears (i.e. bugs, stars, pellets, paper, etc.), green bean in nose, and nervous hair pulling, to name a few. Lo and behold I found a finger nail in an eye, swallowed coins on X-ray, lots of objects in ears (i.e. bugs, stars, pellets, paper, etc.), green bean in a nose, and hair loss from self pulling. Each time that I end up with the same diagnosis as the patient's mother, I think to myself, "Dr. Ray Baker was correct: Mamas are always right!"

....

On the third day there was a wedding in Cana of Galilee, and the mother of Jesus was there. Jesus and his disciples had also been invited to the wedding. When the wine gave out, the mother of Jesus said to him, "They have no wine." And Jesus said to her, "Woman, what concern is that to you and to me? My hour has not yet come."

His mother said to the servants, "Do whatever he tells you." Now standing there were six stone water jars for the Jewish rites of purification, each holding twenty or thirty gallons. Jesus said to them, "Fill the jars with water." And they filled them up to the brim. He said to them, "Now draw some out, and take it to the chief steward." So they took it. When the steward tasted the water that had become wine, and did not know where it came from (though the servants who had drawn the water knew), the steward called the bridegroom and said to him, "Everyone serves the good wine first, and then the inferior wine after the guests have become drunk. But you have kept the good wine until now." Jesus did this, the first of his signs, in Cana of Galilee, and revealed his glory; and his disciples believed in him.

John 2: 1-11

In a chapter dedicated to mothers and the guidance they give, it is important to remember the courage and guidance provided by Mary, the mother of Jesus. She risked public disgrace to be the virgin mother of Jesus with the help of God's guidance.

At the time of the wedding in Cana, very few knew the power of Jesus, but Mary was very aware of his origin and powers. It is hard to believe that of all the miracles Jesus performed while on Earth that the first miracle came about by the pressing of his mother, Mary. Jesus was not sure it was the right time to begin his miracles as he said, "My hour has not yet come." Mary knew Jesus had the power to turn water into wine, and she knew the time was right for Jesus to perform his first miracle. Following the commandment of honoring thy father and mother, Jesus conceded to his mother's wish and provided wine for the wedding.

Jesus may or may not have agreed with the chapter title of 'Mamas are always right', but he certainly followed his mother's lead in this example. God chose well in making Mary the mother of Jesus, as she exemplified courage and faith. Mothers serve a very important role in society and within the family. I have heartfelt appreciation for my mother, my children's mother, mothers of my patients, and the mother of my Lord Jesus.

CHAPTER SEVEN

Fords Only

Mike was a very loyal person. His father owned a Ford dealership in Oakland, Illinois, and Mike would never be caught in anything other than a Ford. He drove a large Ford truck dually, his yard contained two other older Ford trucks, and his carport sported an 1980's Ford Mustang. Lucky for me my father bought a 1965 Ford Mustang for my brothers and me to drive during high school, and of course Mike loved that I had a Ford as well.

Mike's loyalty was not limited to his cars; he showed his loyalty to his customers in multiple ways. One of Mike's customers unfortunately suffered a stroke that left him bedridden, and as an expression of his care, Mike would routinely go to this man's house to give him a haircut. I would have never known Mike did this had it not been for a time when Mike was unable to make it to his maimed customer's home, and he asked me to deliver him a barber's house call. It sounds like a simple act Mike performed, but it was not simple to give this man a haircut, as it took a hydraulic lift just to get him out of bed to cut hair in a very hot non-air conditioned home. Mike also routinely took a deceased customer's wife shopping, as she was unable to make it to the store after her husband's death. It still brings a smile to my face envisioning big Mike pushing a shopping cart up and down each aisle with an elderly friend at his side.

One Christmas morning my family and I were surprised to find Mike Read at the front door. He was delivering fruit baskets to friends and customers. In classic Mike form, he was happy to come inside, have a cup of Swedish Glug, and share some conversation with us prior to moving on to his next delivery. It wasn't quite St. Nick style, but surely St. Mike style. All my family and I still remember the great Christmas morning visit.

Loving sports as he did, Mike would often frequent his customers' high-school sporting events. At least once a season I would see Mike at one of my football and basketball games. I know he did this for other customers as well, as I later compared notes on Mike with friends in college who were also customers of Mike's Barber Shop.

I would be remiss not to mention Mike's loyalty to the University of Georgia Bulldogs. Guaranteed, if the Bulldogs were playing on a Saturday, the voice of the Bulldogs, Larry Munson, would be playing on the radio in 'Mike's Barber Shop.' I was once able to go to a Georgia Football game with my father and Mike, and Mike was in his glory.

The concept of loyalty in medicine sounds very appropriate, but how that relates to day-to-day practice is not so clear. Am I suggesting that house calls should return to routine practice? Certainly that is not an efficient way for doctors to deliver care.

Loyalty in medicine is being there for your patients on a daily basis. There are many days when I don't feel well due to personal illness, muscle strains, or fatigue, but I try to block out my issues to focus on my patients' needs. Loyalty in medicine is going into the hospital at three a.m. to admit a patient who needs to be seen and cared for at that moment, regardless of time of day. Loyalty in medicine is answering phone calls after hours, when fatigue has well set in. Loyalty in medicine is making sure I give my best effort every time I walk in a room with a patient.

I will never forget a pre-game speech delivered by one of my high school football coaches, Ray Allen. My team was just about to take the field against a mediocre opponent, and I'm sure Coach Allen could sense our lack of enthusiasm. Rather than yell and scream at us for not being overly excited, he said, "Not every game is going to be a big game, and you still have to put your hard hat on, pick up your lunch pail, and go to work!" Of course if I were to quote Coach Allen perfectly there would be a lot more "guess what" and "hey" phrases involved. The point was well taken by me if by no one else, and to this day I still hear Coach Allen in my head when there is a time I don't quite feel like doing my job, yet I know it needs to be done.

There certainly have been times when I try to follow Mike Read's lead in expressions of loyalty and care for my patients. I have tried to go to some of my patients' ballgames, help out a patient in need outside of the office, and deliver some random acts of kindness. These acts are certainly not frequent enough, bringing me more self-shame than self pride. I wish I could do more for my patients outside of the context of the office, but the reality is that would likely come at the consequence of less time with my family. The value of some of these acts is more a maintenance of a personal connection that I have and I need to have with my patients. Going to the occasional ballgame helps me remember how fortunate I am to have an impact on the lives of exceptional people. Maybe Mike Read also needed interactions with his customers on a personal level to remind himself why he cut hair each day at 'Mike's Barber Shop'.

....

"The one who enters by the gate is the shepherd of the sheep. The gatekeeper opens the gate for him, and the sheep hear his voice. He calls his own sheep by name and leads them out. When he has brought out all his own, he goes ahead of them, and the sheep follow him because they know his voice."

So again Jesus said to them, "Very truly, I tell you, I am the gate for the sheep. All who came before me are thieves and bandits; but the sheep did not listen to them. I am the gate. Whoever enters by me will be saved, and will come in and go out and find pasture. The thief comes only to steal and kill and destroy. I came that they may have life, and have it abundantly."

"I am the good shepherd. The good shepherd lays down his life for the sheep. The hired hand, who is not the shepherd and does not own the sheep, sees the wolf coming and leaves the sheep and runs away . . ."

John 10: 2-4, 7-12

....

Loyalty is an easy biblical reference to find. The Bible is full of examples of God's loyalty to humankind. I chose the metaphor of the shepherd, because this is the example Jesus gave to understand his commitment to his followers.

During the night, the most vulnerable time, the shepherd would customarily lie at the entry point of the flock, the gatekeeper. This practical position allowed the shepherd to best protect his sheep, and it shows the self-sacrifice of the shepherd for the flock as he would be the first to encounter danger. Clearly this aspect of the metaphor is very appropriate for Jesus' self-sacrifice and protection allotted to his believers.

Jesus says that the shepherd will call his sheep by name. This aspect of the shepherd shows the intimate relationship Jesus has with each of his followers. To imagine Jesus calling me by name brings tears to my eyes and surely makes it easy for me to follow as the sheep follow the shepherd. It is quite powerful that our almighty and loving God knows his flock by name.

The warnings of thieves and bandits hold true in this day and time as well. There are many biblical references of false teachers, and I am reminded of the importance of realizing the possibility of others or our culture's potential to lead me astray. Keeping in God's word and support by other Christians help to keep me in the safety of God's flock.

An image of a hired hand unwilling to protect the flock is unfortunately a true reality. Jesus easily could have fled during times of trial, but he stayed with his flock to the point of self sacrifice. I see this metaphor also true in caring for my children. I appreciate those that help to care for my boys (teachers, coaches, family, and our sitter for date nights), but I know that no one other than my wife and me will fully know and fulfill their needs. God our Father knows each and everyone's needs and provides according to His will. Jesus certainly takes care of his flock like no hired hand would ever do. I thank Jesus for being the great and sacrificial shepherd, and I feel blest to be a part of His flock.

CHAPTER EIGHT

Don't Judge a Barber by His Sign

Driving down Highway 29 in Lilburn, Georgia in the 1980's, you might easily miss 'Mike's Barber Shop.' It was well camouflaged as an old gas station. Kenerly's Hardware, Grocery, and Gas Station was a strip mall before strip malls were hip. The Kenerly's rented half of the old gas house to Mike Read for his barber shop. Outside the old stone gas house hung the barber pole and a black and white sign reading 'Mike's Barber Shop.' It would be easy to look at the outside facade and think that there must not be much good in that shop. Outward appearances can be quite deceiving, especially in Mike's case.

Mike was not keen on updating anything. His clothes, barber chairs, waiting chairs/lawn chairs, desk, sign, and flooring remained unvarying. I take that back: Mike did update the flooring with me as his linoleum flooring installer. My workmanship was poor, as this was my first attempt at such a project, and I cringed in later years as I saw misfit linoleum curl up at the edges. Mike didn't seem to mind, and he sure wasn't going to replace the flooring ever again.

If one were to look at the outward appearances of Mike and his shop, he might never walk in for a haircut, much less see the potential of a future friendship. Luckily I was brought up in a household with minimal prejudgement. To this day I can still hear my grandmother say, "If you can't say anything nice about someone, then don't say anything at all." The initial sight of Mike and his shop was not familiar to me, and I remember it being a bit of an adventure. When I received my first class haircut, I was hooked as a regular customer.

Prejudgement is a powerful behavior. I see people

of all walks of life in my medical practice, and I truly enjoy the diversity of people who walk through the doors. If I were to prejudge these people, I would likely miss out on relationships with all sorts wonderful characters. Living in Athens, a university town, lends itself to diversity. Graduate school especially brings people to town from all over the world, and fortunately for me, a lot of them begin their families during this time, leading some of them to my practice. In addition to the students, there is a wide range of socioeconomic and cultural groups that need a doctor. I routinely tell my patients that I get to live vicariously through their lives via the stories and insights they pass onto me.

Unfortunately I once got to see the power of negative prejudgement created by my own self. I have some patients that have difficult medical conditions that lead to frequent admissions to the hospital. On one occasion I directly admitted a patient to the general medicine floor for a bad diabetic foot wound. After giving orders to the nurse, I gave some commentary along the lines of describing this patient as terribly noncompliant with his medications and medical treatments. Lo and behold, when I went to the medical floor that evening to see the patient and complete my history and physical exam, the nurses were full of reports of how bad this patient was and how noncompliant he seemed. I was a little taken back, as I knew this patient to be a very kind and gentle man, and he had never caused any trouble on the wards on previous admissions. Then I remembered that the nurse was just reflecting back to me the picture that I painted for her during the admission orders. This patient's illness was such, that he continued to require periodic readmissions, and I forever remembered the disservice I did him with his previous admission. On all subsequent admissions I was sure to mention to his nurse how kind this patient was and how sorry I was that he had to endure his disease condition. As you might expect, on all subsequent admissions the nurses would rave to me how nice my patient was, and they were very empathetic to his condition. I truly loved taking care of this particular patient, and to this day I wish I could take back my unfortunate comments, but it taught me a very important lesson on the power of prejudgement.

As I look back on the wonderful people I have had the pleasure of knowing, I thank God for the diversity of those that have impacted my life. Had I succumbed to the power of prejudgement, there is no telling how shallow my understanding of people would be. I have had a great collage of life teachers that have come in different shapes, sizes, ages, races, and occupations. Had my view been too narrow, I might not have ever donned the walls of 'Mike's Barber Shop' and learned the lessons I share with you today. I thank my parents for presenting Mike to me as good and for preparing me to see the good in people.

A leper came to him begging him, and kneeling he said to him, "If you choose, you can make me clean." Moved with pity, Jesus stretched out his hand and touched him, and said to him, "I do choose. Be made clean!" *Immediately the leprosy left him, and he was made clean. After sternly warning him he sent him away at once, saying to him, "See that you say nothing to anyone; but go, show yourself to the priest, and offer for your cleansing what Moses commanded, as a testimony to them." But he went out and began to proclaim if freely, and to spread the word, so that Jesus could no longer go into a town openly, but stayed out in the country; and people came to him from every quarter.*

Mark 1: 40-45

Obviously Jesus was not one to 'Judge a Barber by His Sign.' For those that don't know, leprosy is a horrible disease, causing awful-appearing diffuse skin lesions and ulcerations. It is an infection passed on by contact without a known cure in that time, so those with leprosy in Jesus' day were expected to keep on the outskirts of town to prevent spread of the illness to others. They were perceived as unclean without much sympathy from society.

The simple act of touching a leper was an outward sign of Jesus' unconditional love and compassion. To show compassion to someone whom society has pushed out of sight, shows Jesus' desire to connect and have a relationship to each and every person. It is a good reminder to me as I encounter people with different disfiguring ailments and conditions that these people are also children of God needing a healing hand filled with compassion.

Jesus sure knows how to change preconceptions. Not only does he have the compassion to touch the leper, but he also orders the cleansing of the leper's skin. The power to command a leper be made clean is something this world has never seen. Jesus' next action is hard to imagine in this world of self promotion as he tells the leper to say nothing to anyone other than the priest. The humility of Jesus in a moment of miraculous healing is truly amazing and lays the groundwork for a new kingdom that is unimaginable at that time. I feel fortunate to have a compassionate, humble Lord unwilling to be swayed by societal preconceptions.

CHAPTER NINE

A Broom Can Teach Volumes

Had my mother known that one day I would have a book with the chapter title of "A Broom Can Teach Volumes," she would have likely allowed me to learn this lesson at home. My confession is that this was not a task I routinely did growing up. I was often found cutting the grass, doing dishes, or vacuuming, but sweeping was not among my chores.

As the day passes in the barber shop, hair begins to pile up on the floor, as one might expect. In an attempt to maintain some semblance of cleanliness, Mike Read or Joe Beatty would periodically grab the broom between customers or at the end of the day to clear the floor of hair. After working in barber shops, I quickly realized that sweeping was part of my work duties, and honestly, I was glad to do it. It was actually fun to see how much hair had been cut since the last sweeping. Seeing Mike and Joe step out from their primary role of barber to maintain their barber shops was a good simple lesson in maintaining a business at every level including keeping the floors clean.

My father was a successful business man, working his entire career for Alcan Cable, which made the power lines running along the roads. Alcan was his father's employer as well. When my father graduated from Carthage College, he was hired into a management program with Alcan Cable, which I'm sure sounded very exciting until the first day. It turns out the management training of that day was predicated on allowing the future manager to experience every job within the corporation. I love to hear my father tell the story of his first day at the Alcan Cable Plant in Tucker, Georgia. He walked in as a college graduate, future manager, and he was handed a broom.

Knowing my dad as I do, I'm sure he took it in stride and to this day he would say it was an invaluable experience. As part of my dad's later responsibilities as a Vice President of the company that handed him the broom on day one, he would periodically go to each manufacturing plant and deliver a sort of 'state of the union' type speech. He always felt comfortable talking to the hard-working men and women in the plants, as he had once worked each of their jobs. He likely had good credibility in those settings, thanks in part to the man whom he is, but also thanks to his training at all levels of that corporation.

I would be remiss to not include mothers in a chapter discussing thankless work. From three different perspectives I have been fortunate to see and experience the irreplaceable role of mothers. My mother was a stay-at-home mom and substitute teacher. She was always there to ensure homework was completed, clothes were clean, and meals provided. We used to say she ran a taxi service getting my brothers and me to ball practices and school activities. She always had an open ear as our personal counselor. My wife, Eva, is a wonderful mother to my three sons: Luke, Eli, and Nate. She too is a stay-at-home mother; many days I feel she has worked much harder than I have in providing for the boys. She wears many hats as a tutor, counselor, discipliner, cook, housekeeper, and activity director all under the umbrella of Mom. I have seen my boys thrive during childhood in large part due to her tireless efforts. I have also been able to see the important role of mother in my practice. Matt Baker, MD and I routinely say that if you tell a mama that her baby needs to gain weight, for instance, mama's take care of business. Now sometimes that role of mother comes from a grandmother or aunt or adopted/foster parent. For my patients to grow and develop well, it is in large part due to the efforts of mothers. I try to thank and encourage the mothers in my life and practice for the important work they do each day.

Thank goodness after my first summer working in 'Mike's Barber Shop,' I knew how to use a broom. I headed off to Presbyterian College as a Freshman thinking I would walk onto the basketball team. I played basketball at Brookwood High School in Snellville, Georgia, as what many would call a role player. I was the type of player that would dive for balls, set picks, play defense, and pass well, but I was not given much in the way of the pure talent that most stars in high school and college possess. When I began basketball conditioning at PC without much success, Coach Gregg Nibert graciously offered me a job as the basketball manager. I envisioned a student coach type position, so I jumped at the opportunity, as I knew I didn't have the talent to play with the players at PC. Similar to my father's first day of work, on my first day as the basketball manager, I was handed a broom and asked to sweep the floor prior to practice. My visions of a student coach were quickly erased. I was later introduced to the athletic facilities washer and dryer, and I was educated on the routine of washing the players gear each day. In hindsight, after the experience of being captain of my high school football team and playing varsity basketball, this experience was exactly what I needed. God is good, and He knew I needed humility and an appreciation for all the roles filled in this world. I served as a PC basketball manager all four years of college, and I appreciate the lessons learned from that experience.

There is no better way to gain the respect of a nurse in the Intensive Care Unit than to clean up your critically ill patient up after having a bowel movement in their unconscious state while I try to perform a spinal tap. I expect the nurses to treat my patients well during their watch, and so I too must lead by example and treat my patients as I want them treated when I am not there. Hopefully my nurses today would still be able to attest to my willingness to clean exam room floors soiled with bodily fluids.

I attend church with a former West Point graduate, Rubin Rudisell. He once said that officers are trained that the best way to gain the respect of your men is to do first what no one wants to do, and do last what everyone wants to do. Be the first with a shovel to dig a fox hole, and be the last in line for a hot meal.

As I walk through the hospital on rounds, I try to acknowledge all the staff, but especially the custodial staff. I know what it is like to hold the broom or clean the soiled floors. Their job is crucial to maintaining a place of healing, and I sure appreciate the service they provide each day. To Mike Read, Joe Beatty, Coach Gregg Nibert, my father, my mother, my wife, and mothers in my practice, I thank you for teaching me the power of the broom.

And she (Mary) gave birth to her firstborn son and wrapped him in bands of cloth, and laid him in a manger, because there was no place for them in the inn.

After eight days had passed, it was time to circumcise the child; and he was called Jesus, the name given by the angel before he was conceived in the womb.

Luke 2: 7, 21

And during supper Jesus, knowing that the Father had given all things into his hands, and that he had come from God and was going to God, got up from the table, took off his outer robe, and tied a towel around himself. Then he poured water into a basin and began to wash the disciples' feet and to wipe them with the towel that was tied around him.

After he had washed their feet, had put on his robe, and had returned to the table, he said to them, "Do you know what I have done to you? You call me Teacher and Lord—and you are right, for that is what I am. So if I, your Lord and Teacher, have washed your feet, you also ought to wash one another's feet. For I have set you an example, that you also should do as I have done to you. Very truly, I tell you, servants are not greater than their master, nor are messengers greater than the one who sent them. If you know these things, you are blessed if you do them."

John 13: 3-5, 12-17

....

Then Pilate took Jesus and had him flogged. And the soldiers wove a crown of thorns and put it on his head, and they dressed him in a purple robe. They kept coming up to him saying, "Hail, King of the Jews!" and striking him on the face.

So Jesus came out, wearing the crown of thorns and the purple robe. Pilate said to them, "Here is the man!" When the chief priests and the police saw him, they shouted, "Crucify him! Crucify him!" Pilate said to them, "Take him yourself and crucify him; I find no case against him."

He (Pilate) said to the Jews, "Here is your King!" They cried out, "Away with him! Away with him! Crucify him!" Pilate asked them, "Shall I crucify your King?" The chief priests answered, "We have no king but the emperor." Then he handed him over to them to be crucified.

So they took Jesus; and carrying the cross himself, he went out to what is called The Place of the Skull, which in Hebrew is called Golgotha. There they crucified him . . .

When Jesus knew that all was now finished, he said, "I am thirsty." A jar full of sour wine was standing there. So they put a sponge full of the wine on a branch of hyssop and held it to his mouth. When Jesus had received the wine, he said, "It is finished." Then he bowed his head and gave up his spirit.

John 19: 1-3, 5-6, 14-18, 28-30

The barbers and I know nothing about self-sacrifice compared with Jesus. He is the great example for everything, and no one can claim to be more selfless than Jesus. His life from beginning to end shows examples of abundant love for mankind in the most humble and self sacrificial way.

Over the years I have seen many babies enter this world greeted by poverty or desolate circumstances. I have heard of deliveries at home, in cars, and in emergency rooms, but I have never heard of a baby other than Jesus being delivered in a barn. God sure turned the world on its head by presenting his son, the Messiah, in the most humble birth setting possible. For those who realize their beginnings were bleak, I'm sure it gives comfort to know how the Lord Jesus began life on Earth.

Jesus' act of washing his disciples' feet was not only a good lesson for his disciples, but it is also a wonderful example for this generation as well. In a time of dirt roads and sandal footwear, cleaning feet was certainly a dirty job. During times when my job gets dirty as people cough in my face or babies' diapers need changing during nursery rounds, I am reminded of the tangible example Jesus gave while washing his disciples' feet. His leadership style through service to others was a new dynamic that continues to have a positive impact on society today.

There is no more powerful story in the Bible than the crucifixion of Jesus. He paid the ultimate price for our sins to be forgiven in God's eyes. The crucifixion is the climax of this story, but Jesus suffered greatly leading up to his eventual death on the cross.

Betrayal by one of his own disciples, Judas, begins the pain. The Jewish leaders broke one of their own Ten Commandments by bearing false witness to contain the new direction of the church led by Jesus. The Roman guards severely beat Jesus via the flogging ordered by Pilot. Jesus was mocked with a crown of thorns and a regal colored purple robe over his beaten body. The heavy wooden cross meant for his own crucifixion had to be carried initially by Jesus. Sour wine delivered with a sponge was his comfort while on the cross. This process is brutal and painful to read; imagine how hard it was for his followers and his own mother to watch.

Jesus could have refused to be crucified, but He knew it was God's will for Him to live and to die for humankind. The price He paid on the cross was for man's sin, so that each believer may one day join him in God's kingdom of heaven. This is the ultimate story of self sacrifice. Daily life is filled with acts and events that require self sacrifice and humility; I thank Jesus for his wonderful examples during a well purposed life and an incredible sacrificial death.

A F T E R W O R D

It has been a joy to share some stories of Mike Read and the impact he still has on my life today. Needless to say, it was a trip down memory lane recounting my interactions and observations of Mike. 'Mike's Barber Shop' was a unique throwback establishment owned by a unique throwback individual, Mike Read.

This endeavor is my attempt to share with others some of the lessons I learned from Mike the barber and apply to my Internal Medicine and Pediatrics practice today. It is difficult to know the impact this book may have, but at the very least I hope it gives some guidance to my three sons when they enter their professional lives. I will forever appreciate Mike Read's impact on my life, as well as the other mentors I have been blessed to have over the years, whether mentioned in the book or not.

A great example of an unmentioned mentor is the editor of this book, Dr. H. Dean Thompson. During my days at Presbyterian College, Dr. Thompson was a consistent mentor, teacher, advisor, friend, and even barber shop customer. I enjoyed my days on the front steps of Neville Hall, studying English 101 and 102 with the dynamic teaching style of Dr. Thompson. I will forever be thankful for his impact on my life, and for those that read this book, they will be thankful for his editing skills.

My faith has always been an important part of my life. I enjoyed sharing Biblical examples of the the human truths witnessed in the barber shop. The Biblical examples cited continue to encourage, strengthen, and challenge me daily. Jesus set the standard high, and it is my goal to continue to follow his lead no matter how many times I fall short.

Writing this book has also helped me greatly. It

certainly is helpful to take a moment to think about how I organize my daily life and how I treat others. Some of the lessons have been intuitive to me, but putting this book together has reinforced some patterns that keep my life balanced and enjoyable. Other lessons described are ones that I know, but I need to be more intentional with my adherence.

To my wife, Eva, and three sons—Luke, Eli, and Nate—I thank you for all of the support you give to me. While I have worked on this book, you all have been very positive as you patiently listened to each of my chapters as they were written. The book seemed to be a shared excitement, rather than the family's burden. I should hope "The Barber's Guide to Life, Medicine, and Faith" will be a fun chapter in the book of our life as a family.

To Mike Read, my barber, my friend, I will be forever grateful for your interest in me and especially for the mentorship you provided. I should hope you are with God in Heaven and are at peace. I hope this book is an acceptable testimony to the positive impact you and your barber shop had on others. Thank you, Mike.

To Jesus, my Lord and Savior, I thank you for the wonderful example of how to live during your time on Earth. Although I feel unworthy of your self-sacrificial death for myself and others, I accept the gift and grace granted via this act. I hope this book is pleasing to you. Thank you, Lord.

STUDY GUIDE

My vision for this book is that some will read the book individually for their own interest, yet I envision others reading this in the context of a small group study or in a Sunday school class. With the latter group in mind, I composed a study guide to accompany each chapter to help facilitate group discussion and gain further understanding of God's word. Each chapter would serve as one lesson. In this introduction I will discuss my approach to leading discussion for a chapter. Feel free to utilize this book however it serves you best.

Initially, I open each Sunday school class in prayer. I ask God to help guide the discussion.

Jesus says in Matthew 18:20, "For where two or three are gathered in my name, I am there among them." I always feel confident that the Holy Spirit will help guide the lesson, no pressure.

To open up the class after prayer, I hope everyone will answer the question of the day (QOD). This question is meant to be related to the day's Bible verse in a subtle way. I have found it helps to involve everyone, get to know each other, and aide in utilizing God's word in our daily lives. Obviously if someone can't think of an answer or doesn't want to answer, then a simple "pass" response is sufficient.

Next I would read the barber and doctor correlates. These life lessons will serve as good metaphors or examples of the Bible verses later in each chapter. The reading up to the Bible verses for the chapter takes about five minutes, but again can be referred to when discussing the Biblical passage and life's applications. The goal is to go from knowing God's word to applying His word.

Reading the Biblical passages for the day falls

next in the chapter and would be a good progression from the class' examples of the day's topic (QOD), the barber's example, the doctor's example, and God's example. After reading the Biblical verse the questions in the study guide will relate to the verses for each chapter.

After reading the verses and answering the questions on those verses, I then go back to the chapter and read the discussion of those verses located after the Bible verses in each chapter. I would then see if there was any discussion after reading this section.

Finally, I close the class in prayer. My hope and prayer is to take what is learned in each class and apply to our daily lives. Teaching Sunday school has definitely taught me way more than I could have ever imagined. There is a saying in medicine, "See one, do one, teach one" that seems very applicable to learning God's word.

My classes usually last from thirty to forty-five minutes depending on the discussion for that day. I have truly enjoyed teaching the Bible, and I feel fortunate to have gotten to know my classes well as we study God's word together. I hope this book is helpful to further people along their journey with God.

CHAPTER ONE

Shop Hours

·········· **QOD** ··········

*How do you maintain "Shop Hours"
or do you have any at all?*

Genesis 2: 1-3
Exodus 20: 8-10
Mark 2: 23-24, 27-28
Luke 13: 10-17

- *Is it hard to believe that God took time to rest?*

- *If God took time to rest, what does that say to us
  regarding the need for rest?*

- *What does the fourth commandment of the
  'Ten Commandments' say to you?*

- *How can the fourth commandment help structure
  your week?*

- *Does anyone's work or occupation require that they
  work on Sunday?*

- *If the need to work on Sunday is unavoidable, how can accommodations be made to honor God's commandment?*

- *Describe one way you can rearrange you daily life to achieve:*

Shop Hours
Shades Open: Open
Shades Closed: Closed

Have a good week!

CHAPTER TWO

I'll Rush When It's Your Turn

QOD

When do you routinely feel rushed?

Luke 10: 38-42

- *Do you ever feel like Martha?*

- *What activities commonly distract you?*

- *What does Jesus mean by "there is need of only one thing?"*

- *Are there times when Martha is needed?*

- *When do we need to emulate Mary?*

- *Is it possible to be productive like Martha and be focused on God like Mary?*

- *Are there times in your life when you need to use barber Joe's line, "I'll rush when it is your turn?"*

Accept God's gift of patience this week!

CHAPTER THREE

When You First Start, Don't Take Off Too Much

······· **QOD** ·······

Recall a time or situation that makes you feel overwhelmed.

1 Corinthians 10: 13

- *Is there comfort in knowing that others face similar challenges to yours?*

- *How is it helpful to know others are tested in the way you are tested?*

- *Does Paul understand struggle?*

- *Has Jesus endured times of testing?*

- *How can Paul's words reassure you during your times of struggle?*

- *How can we approach our routine times of stress with Mike Read's advice to a beginning barber, "When you first start, don't take off too much?"*

Remember God is with you this week!

CHAPTER FOUR

No Fad Haircuts

.... **QOD** ....

*Can you recall a time when you felt like you
were being asked to cross a moral boundary?*

....

Matthew 4: 1-11

- *Why did God allow Jesus to be tempted by Satan?*

- *What is significant about the timing of Jesus'
  testing in respect to His forty days of fasting in the
  wilderness and in respect to Jesus' ministry?*

- *How did Satan tempt Jesus initially?*

- *What was Satan's second temptation toward Jesus?*

- *What was significant about Satan's third temptation?*

- *What defense did Jesus use to ward off Satan's
  temptations?*

- *Using Jesus' example, how can we prepare ourselves
  for the temptation of sin in our lives?*

- *Are there areas in your personal or professional life that require clear communication like Mike Read's "No Fad Haircuts" sign?*

Be God's witness this week!

CHAPTER FIVE

Blending Is the Key to a Good Haircut

Can you describe a time or situation that requires you to be flexible and change direction for success?

Matthew 15: 1-2, 10-11, 15-20

- *In the Jewish religion what is the role of the Pharisee?*

- *What was Jesus trying to teach the Pharisees?*

- *How had the execution of the Jewish Old Testament Law gotten off track?*

- *How can we apply the explanation Jesus gave to Peter in our daily lives?*

- *A haircut sometimes requires the barber to take a new direction and utilize the skill of blending. Using the Holy Spirit as our guide how do we redirect or potentially avoid our life's miscues?*

Be God's light to the world this week!

CHAPTER SIX

Mamas Are Always Right

···························· **QOD** ····························

*Can you recall a time where you had to
say to yourself, "Mom was right?"*

John 2: 1-11

- *Is it difficult to envision Jesus as a son of Mary?*

- *God chose Mary as the mother of Jesus, why Mary?*

- *What is unique about a mother's perspective?*

- *In these verses how did Jesus follow one of God's Ten
  Commandments, honor your father and mother?*

- *As the first miracle in Jesus' ministry, why was Jesus
  hesitant to perform this miracle?*

- *Mike Read listened to the mamas. Ray Baker, MD
  listened to the mamas. How can you better listen to
  the mamas in your life?*

Walk with God in your daily lives!

CHAPTER SEVEN

Fords Only

.... **QOD** ....

As Mike was loyal to Fords, to what would others say you are loyal?

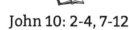

John 10: 2-4, 7-12

- *What characteristics of the dynamic between the shepherd and his sheep brings comfort in thinking of Jesus as our shepherd?*

- *Could you pick your parents' voice out of a crowd, or can your children easily recognize your voice?*

- *Jesus called his disciples by name to follow Him, how is this similar to the shepherd calling his sheep?*

- *How can you be loyal to Jesus, recognizing his voice when He calls?*

Be loyal to God this week!

CHAPTER EIGHT

Don't Judge a Barber by His Sign

QOD

*Can you recall a person that totally defied
your initial impression?*

Mark 1: 40-45

- *How were lepers treated in Biblical times?*

- *Are there disease conditions today that create a
  similar community response?*

- *What was remarkable in Jesus' physical response
  to the leper?*

- *Can you imagine the emotions experienced by
  the leper?*

- *How did Jesus respond to the healing and what does
  that say about Jesus?*

- *Based on the appearance of 'Mike's Barber Shop' it
  would be hard to imagine such a great barber and
  person was inside. How can you avoid missing out
  on knowing the Mike Reads of this world?*

Show God's compassion this week!

CHAPTER NINE

A Broom Can Teach Volumes

.... **QOD** ....

Have you ever worked a job or served a role that was very necessary, but required much self-sacrifice and humility?

....

Luke 2: 7, 21
John 13: 3-5, 12-17
John 19: 1-3, 5-6, 14-18, 28-30

- *Jesus had a very humble entrance into this world; why do you think God presented Jesus in this fashion?*

- *How did Jesus summarize his revolutionary leadership style in the John 13 passage?*

- *How is this different from the paradigm of Leader, King, or Lord of that day?*

  Of today?

- *Consider the dramatic contrast of the triumphant procession of Palm Sunday preceding the painful, humiliating events leading up to Jesus' crucifixion.*

- *Consider the level of dedication and self-sacrifice Jesus had for us.*

- *Did Jesus submit to his betrayal and crucifixion, knowing it was the will of God?*

  How can we follow Jesus' examples of humility?

  Self-sacrifice?

  Devotion to God?

Walk with awareness of God's love for you this week and beyond!

CPSIA information can be obtained
at www.ICGtesting.com
Printed in the USA
LVOW04s0324290916

506614LV00014B/84/P